Sight Word Tales™

many kind
which buy

P9-DBX-938

So Many Kinds of Shoes!

by Maria Fleming
illustrated by Beccy Blake

SCHOLASTIC INC.

New York • Toronto • London • Auckland • Sydney
Mexico City • New Delhi • Hong Kong • Buenos Aires

No part of this publication may be reproduced, stored in a retrieval system, or transmitted in any form or by any means, electronic, mechanical, photocopying, recording, or otherwise, without written permission of the publisher. For information regarding permission, write to Scholastic Inc., Attention: Permissions Department, 557 Broadway, New York, NY 10012.

Designed by Maria Lilja
ISBN-13: 978-0-545-01666-7 • ISBN-10: 0-545-01666-5
Copyright © 2008 by Scholastic Inc.
All rights reserved. Printed in China.

First printing, January 2008

12 11 10 9 8 7 6 5 4 3   11 12 13/0

Sight Words Fact

Sight words are words that you see again and again when you read. This book is filled with the sight words **many**, **kind**, **which**, and **buy**. Look for them in the text. Check the pictures, too!

Spider needs to **buy** new shoes.
Which kind of shoes will Spider choose?

Will she **buy** the **kind** for running races?

Or maybe I will **buy** this **kind**.

Will she **buy** the **kind** with purple laces?

So **many** different **kinds** of shoes!
Which kind of shoes will Spider choose?

Will she **buy** the **kind** to dance ballet?

Will she **buy** the **kind** for a rainy day?

So **many** different **kinds** of shoes!
Which kind of shoes will Spider choose?

Will she **buy** the **kind** with noisy taps?

Will she **buy** the **kind** with flowered straps?

So **many** different **kinds** of shoes!
Which kind of shoes will Spider choose?

Many shoes, but **many** feet.
Many feet just can't be beat!

Spider has made up her mind.
She **buys** one of every **kind**!

Sight Word Review

many which
kind buy

Do you know the four sight words in this book? Read aloud the word on each shoe.

many

buy

many   kind   which

which   buy   kind

Sight Word Fill-ins

Listen to the sentences. Then choose a sight word from the box to fill in each blank.

Word Box   many   which   kind   buy

1 He has _____ friends.

2 Tell me _____ one you want.

3 What _____ of dog is that?

4 We went to the store to _____ milk.

5 How _____ pennies are in the jar?

6 Vanilla is her favorite _____ of ice cream.

7 He will _____ new sneakers today.

8 I don't know _____ way to go.

Sight Word Cheers

Celebrate the new sight words you learned by saying these four short cheers.

M-a-n-y! Give a yell!
What do these four letters spell?
A sight word that we all know well —
Many, many, many!

W-h-i-c-h! Give a yell!
What do these five letters spell?
A sight word that we all know well —
Which, which, which!

K-i-n-d! Give a yell!
What do these four letters spell?
A sight word that we all know well —
Kind, kind, kind!

B-u-y! Give a yell!
What do these three letters spell?
A sight word that we all know well —
Buy, buy, buy!